rockschool®

Drums Grade 4

Performance pieces, technical exercises and in-depth guidance
for Rockschool examinations

Acknowledgements

Published by Rockschool Ltd. © 2012
Catalogue Number RSK051223
ISBN: 978-1-908920-22-5

AUDIO
Recorded at Fisher Lane Studios
Produced and engineered by Nick Davis
Assistant engineer and Pro Tools operator Mark Binge
Mixed and mastered at Langlei Studios
Additional editing and mixing by Duncan Jordan
Supporting Tests recorded by Duncan Jordan and Kit Morgan
Mastered by Duncan Jordan
Executive producers James Uings, Jeremy Ward and Noam Lederman

MUSICIANS
James Arben, Joe Bennett, Jason Bowld, Larry Carlton, Stuart Clayton, Andy Crompton, Neel Dhorajiwala, Fergus Gerrand, Charlie Griffiths, Felipe Karam, Kishon Khan, Noam Lederman, DJ Harry Love, Dave Marks, Kit Morgan, Jon Musgrave, Jake Painter, Richard Pardy, Ross Stanley, Stuart Ryan, Carl Sterling, Henry Thomas, Camilo Tirado, Simon Troup, James Uings, Steve Walker, Chris Webster, Norton York, Nir Z

PUBLISHING
Fact Files written by Luke Aldridge, Jason Bowld, Neel Dhorajiwala, Stephen Lawson, Noam Lederman and David West
Walkthroughs written by Noam Lederman
Music engraving and book layout by Simon Troup and Jennie Troup of Digital Music Art
Proof and copy editing by Noam Lederman, Claire Davies, Stephen Lawson, Simon Pitt and James Uings
Publishing administration by Caroline Uings
Cover design by Philip Millard

SYLLABUS
Syllabus director: Jeremy Ward
Instrumental specialists: Stuart Clayton, Noam Lederman and James Uings
Special thanks to: Brad Fuller and Georg Voros

SPONSORSHIP
Noam Lederman plays Mapex Drums, PAISTE cymbals and uses Vic Firth Sticks
Rockschool would like to thank the following companies for donating instruments used in the cover artwork

PRINTING
Printed and bound in the United Kingdom by Caligraving Ltd
CDs manufactured in the European Union by Software Logistics

DISTRIBUTION
Exclusive Distributors: Music Sales Ltd

CONTACTING ROCKSCHOOL
www.rockschool.co.uk
Telephone: +44 (0)845 460 4747
Fax: +44 (0)845 460 1960

Table of Contents

Introductions & Information

Rockschool Grade Pieces

Technical Exercises

Supporting Tests

Additional Information

Welcome to Rockschool Drums Grade 4

Welcome to Drums Grade 4

Welcome to the Rockschool Drums Grade 4 pack. This book and CD contain everything you need to play drums at this grade. In the book you will find the exam scores in drum notation. The CD has full stereo mixes of each tune, backing tracks to play along to for practice and spoken two bar count-ins to both the full mixes and backing track versions of the songs. There are two backing tracks of each song: one with a click and one without. You can choose which one to play along with in the exam.

Drum Exams

At each grade, you have the option of taking one of two different types of examination:

- **Grade Exam:** a Grade Exam is a mixture of music performances, technical work and tests. You prepare three pieces (two of which may be Free Choice Pieces) and the contents of the Technical Exercise section. This accounts for 75% of the exam marks. The other 25% consists of: *either* a Sight Reading *or* an Improvisation & Interpretation test (10%), a pair of instrument specific Ear Tests (10%) and finally you will be asked five General Musicianship Questions (5%). The pass mark is 60%.

- **Performance Certificate:** in a Performance Certificate you play five pieces. Up to three of these can be Free Choice Pieces. Each song is marked out of 20 and the pass mark is 60%.

Book Contents

The book is divided into a number of sections. These are:

- **Exam Pieces:** in this book you will find six specially commissioned pieces of Grade 4 standard. Each of these is preceded by a *Fact File*. Each Fact File contains a summary of the song, its style, tempo, key and technical features, along with a list of the musicians who played on it. There is additional information on the techniques and style as well as recommended further listening. The song itself is printed on two pages. Immediately after each song is a *Walkthrough*. This covers the song from a performance perspective, focusing on the technical issues you will encounter. Each Walkthrough features two graphical musical 'highlights' showing particular parts of the song. Each song comes with a full mix version and a backing track. Both versions have spoken count-ins at the beginning. Please note that any solos played on the full mix versions are indicative only.

- **Technical Exercises:** you should prepare the exercises set in this grade as indicated. There is also a Fill test that should be practised and played to the backing track.

- **Supporting Tests and General Musicianship Questions:** in Drums Grade 4 there are three supporting tests – *either* a Sight Reading *or* an Improvisation & Interpretation test and two Ear Tests – and a set of General Musicianship Questions (GMQs) asked at the end of each exam. Examples of the types of tests likely to appear in the exam are printed in this book. Additional test examples of both types of test and the GMQs can be found in the Rockschool *Companion Guide To Drums*.

- **Grade 5 Preview:** we have included in this book one of the songs found in the Grade 5 Drums book as a taster. The piece is printed with its Fact File and Walkthrough, and the full mix and backing tracks can be found on the CD.

- **General Information:** finally, you will find information on exam procedures, including online examination entry, marking schemes, and what to do when arriving, and waiting, for your exam.

We hope you enjoy using this book. You will find a *Syllabus Guide* for Drums and other exam information on our website: *www.rockschool.co.uk*. Rockschool Graded Music Exams are accredited in England, Wales and Northern Ireland by Ofqual, the DfE and CCEA and by SQA Accreditation in Scotland.

SONG TITLE: NOISY NEIGHBOUR

GENRE: INDIE

TEMPO: 135 BPM

TECH FEATURES: OFF-BEAT HI-HAT GROOVE
RIDING ON THE TOMS
CHOKE CYMBAL

COMPOSER: NOAM LEDERMAN

PERSONNEL: STUART RYAN (GTR)
DAVE MARKS (BASS)
NOAM LEDERMAN (DRUMS/ PERCUSSION)

OVERVIEW

'Noisy Neighbour' is an indie rock track written in the style of groups like Arctic Monkeys, Franz Ferdinand and The Strokes. It features an off-beat hi-hat groove, riding on the toms and a choke cymbal among its techniques.

STYLE FOCUS

Indie drummers like to keep busy during a song, often playing 16th notes on either the hi-hat or on the toms. The style may well have the greater part of its roots planted in disco, but it has been distilled through British new wave acts including the short-lived but timeless Joy Division and synth rock band New Order who combined dance beats with guitars. The latter's drummer, Stephen Morris, helped influence the whole dance rock movement by mixing samples and drum machines with his own playing. Tempos tend to be fast (occasionally bordering on frenetic) and should be played loud.

THE BIGGER PICTURE

In the late 1980s through to the early 1990s, the bands of the 'Madchester' scene, (a term created to describe a Manchester-based genre of music that combined alt rock, psychedelic rock and dance music) such as The Stone Roses, Happy Mondays and Inspiral Carpets, mixed guitars with dance grooves but by 2000 most of them had disbanded.

The void was filled by Franz Ferdinand and Arctic Monkeys, who brought guitars back into nightclubs. The Strokes' fuzzy brand of indie rock made them flavour of the year with their 2001 debut *Is This It*, while Hard-Fi's potent blend of hooks, anthemic choruses and indie guitars took them to the top of the UK charts in 2007 with *Once Upon A Time In The West*. The music had a punk-like urgency and the direct simplicity of garage rock in terms of its chords and structures, but it was still danceable.

RECOMMENDED LISTENING

Whatever People Say I Am, That's What I'm Not (2006) by the Arctic Monkeys was the fastest selling UK debut album ever thanks to 'I Bet You Look Good On The Dancefloor'. Franz Ferdinand's 'Take Me Out', from their self-titled 2004 debut, uses a 16th-note disco pattern and hi-hat accents played off the downbeat as seen in 'Noisy Neighbour.' 'Last Night', from The Strokes' first album, is a catchy garage rock track propelled by a driving beat.

Noisy Neighbour

Noam Lederman

Drums Grade 4

[23]

Develop

[27]

[31]

D

[35]

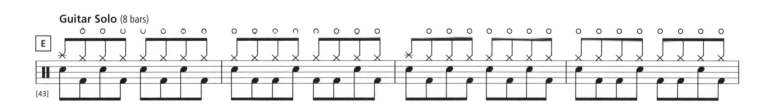

[39]

Guitar Solo (8 bars)

E

[43]

D.%. al Coda ⊕

[47]

⊕ **Coda**

[51]

Walkthrough

A Section (Bars 1–8)
This section features an energetic indie beat played on the floor tom, bass drum and snare.

Pick-up fill | *Syncopation*
The pick-up fill accents the first beat and the offbeats of the second and fourth beats. This offbeat accent creates a syncopated feel that can be challenging to synchronise precisely. Between the crash cymbal accents there are groups of four 16th notes of the snare. Aim to play these evenly and count the full rhythmic value of the first and second crashes. The fill is in a pick-up bar and should therefore be played during the second bar of the spoken count-in (Fig. 1).

Bar 1 | *Floor tom groove*
First work on the rhythms used in this groove then choose and experiment with the sticking option that feels most comfortable according to your technique. Add the quarter note bass drums and ensure the dynamic level *mp* is applied as indicated in the music.

B Section (Bars 10–18)
In this section you will find quarter-note stabs, fills and a cymbal choke.

Bar 11 | *Choke*
When the word choke appears above a cymbal note it means that the natural decay of the cymbal must be stopped by grabbing it straight after hitting it. The most efficient way to perform this technique is to grab the cymbal with the opposite hand to the one used to strike it. This is used in many styles and is most common to the crash cymbal.

C Section (Bars 19–34)
The first eight bars of this section consist of an off-beat hi-hat groove. From bar 27, the drum part needs to be developed in keeping with the style of the piece.

Bar 20 | *Offbeat hi-hat groove*
In this bar, all the hi-hats are played on the offbeats. Therefore, you will not be able to rely on the hi-hat as your anchor. Instead, use the simple bass drum and snare pattern to keep the pulse steady and focus on playing all the offbeat hi-hats accurately.

Bars 27–34 | *Development*
In order to create more intensity, try playing a busier groove and adding crashes and punchy fills, but make sure that your continuity is not affected. There is no harm in planning your development ideas. However, remember that any improvised sections need to sound fluent, effortless and convincing. They must also be in keeping with the style of the piece.

D Section (Bars 35–42)
This is a similar pattern to the one introduced in section B but this time improvised fills are required.

Bar 36 | *Fill*
The word fill indicates that you have to play a stylistic improvised pattern in the assigned gap. Fills should be performed with accuracy and confidence, and should be in keeping with the style of the piece. Listen to Arctic Monkeys drummer Matt Helders to gain some ideas for improvised fills in this style.

E Section (Bars 43–52)
This section includes an eight bar guitar solo, a reprise of the intro and a two bar ending with accented stabs. When returning to 𝄋 in bar 1, do not play the part as written. Instead, add your personal interpretation and develop it.

Bar 44 | *Heavy 3:3:2*
In this groove the snare and bass drum pattern is divided into three groups of three, three and two eighth notes. The snare plays on the first eighth note in each group and the bass drum fills in between. Make sure you are comfortable with this hand and foot co-ordination before adding the open hi-hat. This groove develops in bar 48 where each snare is played with a crash cymbal. Your movement between the crash and open hi-hat must be quick or else your synchronisation to the track will be affected (Fig. 2).

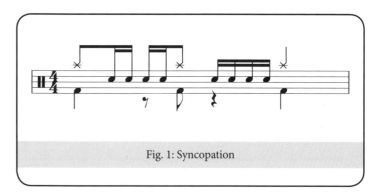

Fig. 1: Syncopation

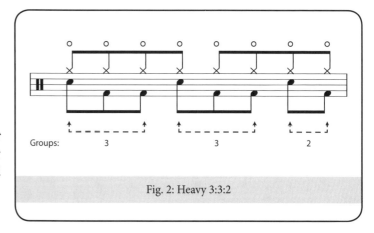

Fig. 2: Heavy 3:3:2

SONG TITLE: COLD PANTS

GENRE: FUNK

TEMPO: 112 BPM

TECH FEATURES: SNARE GHOST NOTES

OPEN HI-HAT

DRAGS

COMPOSER: LUKE ALDRIDGE

PERSONNEL: STUART RYAN (GTR)

HENRY THOMAS (BASS)

NOAM LEDERMAN (DRUMS)

ROSS STANLEY (KEYS)

FULL FAT HORNS (BRASS)

FERGUS GERRAND (PERC)

OVERVIEW

'Cold Pants' is an instrumental funk written in the style of James Brown, Maceo Parker and Fred Wesley. It features drags, snare ghost notes, and open hi-hat among its techniques.

STYLE FOCUS

This piece contains a selection of typical James Brown style grooves, as played by his classic rhythm sections featuring Clyde Stubblefield, John 'Jabo' Starks and Melvin Parker. During some concerts, Brown recruited two of his drummers to play at once to enhance the groove and feel of particular songs.

The first groove in 'Cold Pants' is a standard funk beat that adds the open hi-hat the second time round and has a distinct 'Sex Machine' vibe.

In the bridge there is a more syncopated idea where the 2 on the snare is delayed until the 'and' of 2 so that it's played in time with the hits from the horns. While the solo section is reminiscent of the signature groove from 'Cold Sweat', you can explore the groove in the development section that gives it that classic James Brown drum break feel.

THE BIGGER PICTURE

Brown enjoyed success as a gospel and R&B artist in the 1950s and early 1960s before developing into a soul singer and inventing funk in the late 1960s. His classic line-up during that period included the aforementioned drummers Stubblefield, Starks and Parker. The drum break heard in many of his hits became the foundation of the breakbeats used in early hip hop. It is also said that Brown's vocal style, a highly rhythmic combination of speaking and singing, also had an influence on what would eventually become rap.

RECOMMENDED LISTENING

Brown's singles 'Cold Sweat' and 'Hot Pants' inspired this track and are essential. 'Sex Machine' is also hinted at but most of Brown's back catalogue is worth investigating. Maceo Parker's 1992 live album, *Life On Planet Groove*, is a great place to start for his solo work. Soulive's 2001 debut album, *Doin' Something*, features another Brown drummer Fred Wesley and there is a clear James Brown influence on 'Tonight' from their 2009 recording *Up Here*. Finally, the Lettuce albums *Outta Here* (2001) and *Rage* (2008) display a more contemporary funk sound.

Cold Pants

Luke Aldridge

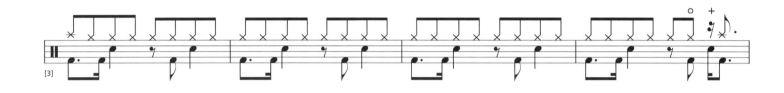

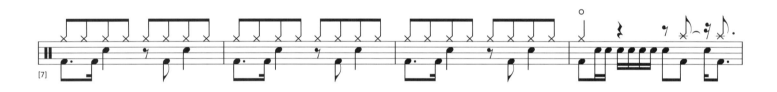

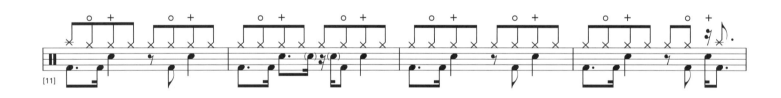

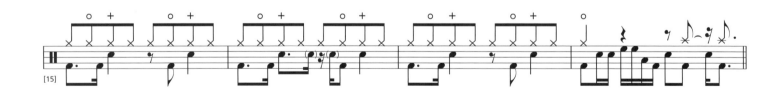

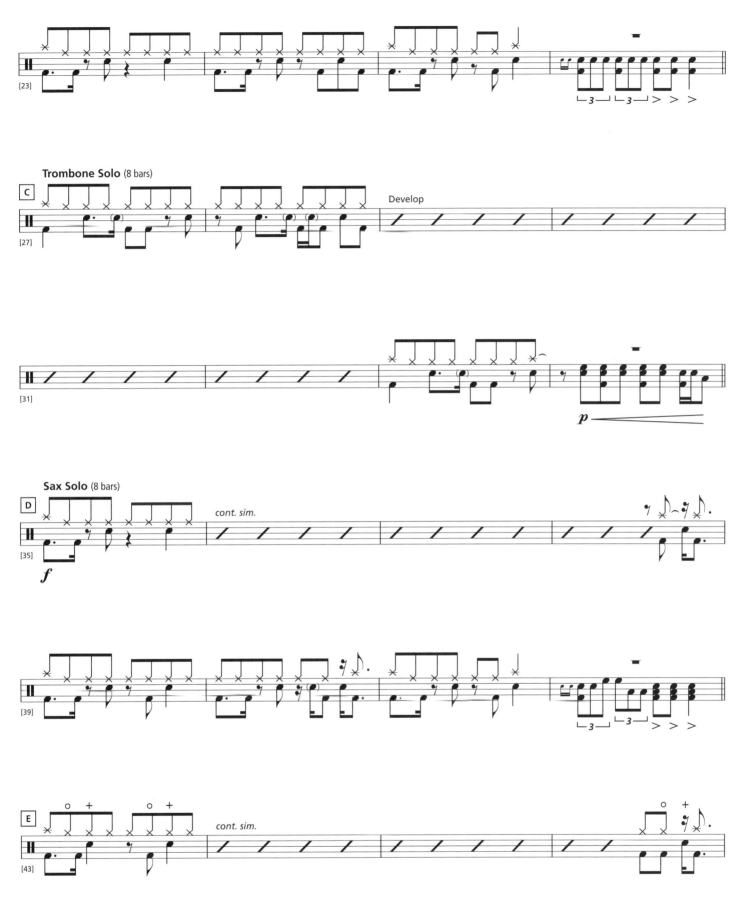

Walkthrough

A section (Bars 1–18)
Following the initial two bar stabs, the verse funk groove is introduced in bar 3. This groove includes consistent eighth note hi-hats, backbeat snare, syncopated crashes and a varied bass drum pattern.

Bar 3 | *16th-note bass drum*
In this funk groove the 16th-note bass drum is placed between the second and third eighth note hi-hats. Co-ordinate this well and ensure the flow of the hi-hats and groove is not affected.

Bar 10 | *Syncopated pushes*
There are two syncopated pushes in this bar placed on the '&' of beat three and the 'e' of beat four. The pushes should be played with the crash and bass drum following a snare on the beat. Studying this pattern before attempting the whole piece is useful because it's used throughout the song (Fig. 1).

Bar 12 | *Ghost notes*
Ghost notes are marked with brackets and are usually played on the snare drum. The dynamic level of the ghost notes should be much lower than the regular snare strokes because if they are played too loudly they will interrupt the flow of the groove. Ghost notes are performed as a 'tap', where your hand is kept close to the drum head and there is no need to lift it before executing the stroke. Once you've achieved the ghost note sound, focus on co-ordinating these accurately between the eighth note hi-hats.

B Section (Bars 19–26)
The second main groove is introduced in the bridge section. This funk groove is played on the ride cymbal with displaced snare and 16th-note bass drums.

Bar 26 | *Changing rhythms*
Following the open drag there are triplets, eighth notes and a quarter note to perform. Changing fluently between the rhythms might require preparation. Break down the fill into individual beats and slowly reconstruct it while using a metronome. The suggested sticking is alternate starting with the right, but if there is another option that feels more comfortable according to your technique then use it (Fig. 2).

C Section (Bars 27–34)
In this section there is an eight bar trombone solo. The drum groove needs to be developed in keeping with the style and the crescendo fill in bar 34 must be observed.

Bar 34 | *Crescendo fill*
This fill starts on the second eighth note of beat one. However, counting the beats is vital because it follows a syncopated crash from the previous bar. The first snare/high tom stroke in the fill must be confident but played in the dynamic level '***p***', which stands for soft. The dynamic mark that follows ***p*** is referred to as 'crescendo', which means to gradually get louder.

D Section (Bars 35–42)
The solo section continues with a sax solo of eight bars. This groove is similar to the one introduced in the bridge section but variations can be made where cont. sim. is marked.

Bar 42 | *Sticking*
There are various sticking patterns that can be used in the first two triplets. If you prefer using single strokes, follow either R L R L R L or R L R L R R. The first option requires fast left hand movement in order to play the unison on beat three well. The second demands reliable right hand technique. You can also choose to play the triplets with doubles (R R L L R R) because this is seen as a musical application of one of the technical exercises in this grade (see Rudiments, Hands & Feet Patterns on p.29).

E Section (Bars 43–50)
This is the reprise of the verse but variations should be added. The improvised fill in bar 49 gives you the opportunity to display your understanding of the style, technical ability and musicality.

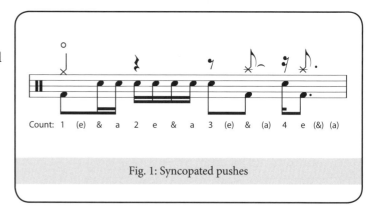

Fig. 1: Syncopated pushes

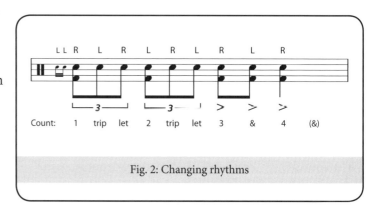

Fig. 2: Changing rhythms

SONG TITLE: ATTITUDE

GENRE: CLASSIC ROCK

TEMPO: 105 BPM

TECH FEATURES: TOM-BASED GROOVE

RIDE CYMBAL BELL

16TH-NOTE HI-HAT GROOVE

COMPOSERS: JAMES UINGS &

KUNG FU DRUMMER

PERSONNEL: STUART RYAN (GUITAR)

HENRY THOMAS (BASS)

NOAM LEDERMAN (DRUMS)

OVERVIEW

'Attitude' is a track in the style of the classic hard rock bands of the 1980s, led by the likes of Guns N' Roses and Mötley Crüe, and their 1970s predecessors KISS. It features a tom-based groove, single strokes on the hi-hat and use of the bell of the ride cymbal among its techniques.

STYLE FOCUS

This style of classic rock should be played in a more eclectic manner than your usual straight rock style. Several different feels need to be performed to create a colourful drum track. Swung feels, 16th-note hi-hat grooves, straight, accented grooves with big crash accents and syncopated ride patterns are some of the many shapes you'll need to throw in order to encompass this style. Steven Adler of Guns N' Roses and Stephen Perkins of Jane's Addiction are both great examples of this.

THE BIGGER PICTURE

Rock in the 1980s was dominated by the bands that came out of Los Angeles, led by Guns N' Roses who shot to fame with their snarling debut *Appetite*

For Destruction. They built on the blueprint of 1970s giants like KISS, Aerosmith and Ted Nugent by adding the sneer and aggression of punk to the rock 'n' roll format.

For drummers, the big, extravagant set-ups of the 1970s stadium drummers were replaced by smaller kits that reflected the music's origins in the Los Angeles club circuit. The playing was not technically demanding or chops heavy, but required a great feel for groove and plenty of power.

As the new bands became stadium fillers in their own right, their drummers indulged their own sense of the spectacular, the highlight of which was Tommy Lee's rollercoaster drum riser with Mötley Crüe.

RECOMMENDED LISTENING

Guns N' Roses *Appetite For Destruction* is essential listening. Steven Adler's tom groove in 'Mr Brownstone' is a particular highlight. Mötley Crüe's classic 'Dr Feelgood' is a lesson in big rock drumming and 'Wild Side' features Tommy Lee playing his hi-hat with alternating single strokes. 'Poison Ivy' from Faster Pussycat's album *Wake Me When It's Over* is a great example of how to play a straight rock pattern with a swing feel.

Attitude

James Uings & Kung Fu Drummer

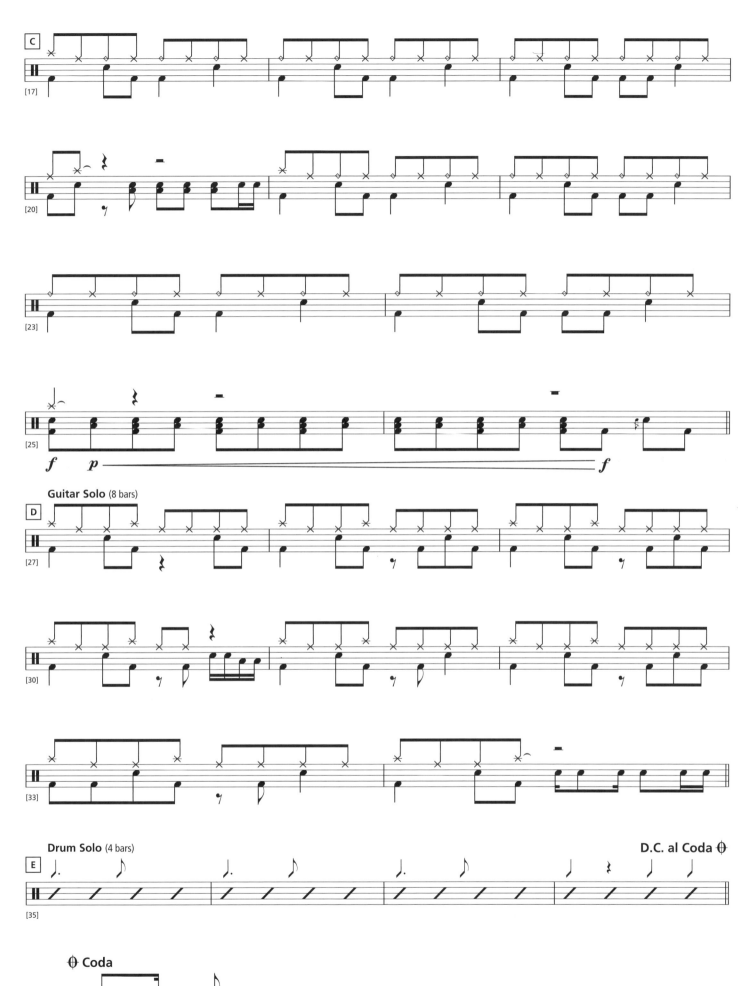

Walkthrough

A Section (Bars 1–8)
This section features an energetic rock beat played on the bass drum, snare and toms.

Bar 2 | *Slightly swung*
Two things are crucial here: playing the voices written with the accents and playing with the correct feel. Slightly swung 16th notes should sound like the middle ground between swung and straight feel. This is an advanced technique used in second line New Orleans beats. Get familiar with the straight and swung feels first and then practise the slightly swung until it feels right.

Bar 8 | *Change to a straight feel*
After playing the syncopated stabs accurately, focus on the fourth beat. The eighth note snare flam on the beat is followed by two 16th notes on the floor tom. These 16th notes are the first notes of the straight feel groove in bar 9.

B Section (Bars 9–16)
In this section the groove moves to the hi-hat but the 16th-note rhythm is maintained.

Bar 10 | *16th-note hi-hat groove*
This type of groove should be played with alternate sticking and your right hand needs to move from the hi-hat to the snare to play the backbeat. Co-ordinating the bass drum with hi-hat strokes played with your left hand (beat one) is probably the biggest challenge in this bar. Practise it slowly and ensure it is executed with perfect unison (Fig. 1).

C Section (Bars 17–26)
This section consists mostly of a solid ride cymbal groove with a combination of ride and bell sounds.

Bar 18 | *Bell of ride*
The cymbal notation in this bar indicates that consistent eighth notes should be played on the ride and bell sounds (the bell on every beat and the ride on every offbeat). To achieve solid projection from the bell, use the neck part of your drum stick and strike with conviction. Use wrist motion rather than arm to ensure the movement between the bell and ride is fluent and efficient. A master of this technique is the drummer Vinnie Colaiuta. Watching videos of him can help you make the minor adjustments needed in order to perform this effortlessly (Fig. 2).

Bars 25–26 | *Crescendo fill*
The first hit in bar 25 should be played loud, then on the second eighth note drop to p (soft) and gradually build up to f (loud). This is a dramatic moment typical of this style, so practise it well and make it sound big.

D Section (Bars 27–34)
Here is the guitar solo section where the groove is played on the ride cymbal with crashes and fills.

Bar 34 | *Rhythmic displacement*
The fill in this bar consists of three groups of two 16th notes. These should be played with a 16th-note rest between them. Ensure this rhythmic displacement does not affect the pulse.

E Section (Bars 35–39)
This starts with a four bar drum solo around the written stabs then there is a reprise of the introduction and a one bar ending with syncopated crashes. When returning to the start of the piece after the drum solo, don't play the part as written. Instead, add your own interpretation and develop it.

Bars 35–38 | *Drum solo*
Improvisation over rhythmic stabs is common in this style. Listen to the track to learn where the stabs are placed. You can also look at the drum chart if you prefer to read the rhythms. Improvise between the stabs, demonstrate your technical ability and musicality, and keep the pulse steady.

Bar 39 | *Syncopated rhythm*
The rhythm in beats one and two should be counted as '3 – -& a – – &'. The accents on the 'a' and '&' give the syncopation feel to the phrase. Listen carefully to the guitar and bass on the track and synchronise accurately with them.

Fig. 1: 16th-note hi-hat groove

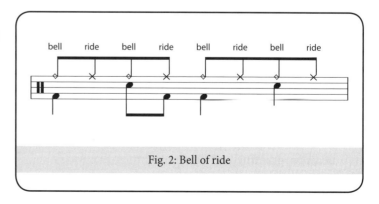

Fig. 2: Bell of ride

SONG TITLE: THE NOD

GENRE: HIP HOP

TEMPO: 95 BPM

TECH FEATURES: 16TH-NOTE GROOVES & FILLS
CROSS STICK
RIM-SHOTS

COMPOSER: NEEL DHORAJIWALA

PERSONNEL: NEEL DHORAJIWALA (PROD)
NOAM LEDERMAN (DRUMS)
FERGUS GERRAND (PERC)
HENRY THOMAS (BASS)
HARRY LOVE (DJ)

OVERVIEW

'The Nod' is a hip hop track in the style of artists from America's East Coast such as The Roots, Nas and Gang Starr. It features cross stick, rim-shots as well as 16th-note grooves and fills among its techniques.

STYLE FOCUS

Unlike gangsta rap, which employed live musicians in many of its recordings, East Coast hip hop was produced traditionally using drum machines and samplers. However, many hip hop acts prefer to use live drums onstage. The result is a human groove coupled with a machine-like feel and approach to the drum part. Emulating the straight quantization of a drum machine or the swing feel of an Akai MPC sampler might sound like a simple task, but actually achieving a balance of human and drum machine feel is a difficult skill to master.

THE BIGGER PICTURE

Hip hop was created in New York in the late 1970s and spread across America's East Coast in the early 1980s. East Coast hip hop is characterised by heavy beats programmed on drum machines, like Akai's

MPC, and by its creative use of samples. Purists consider it to be the original, and therefore best, form of hip hop. However, that's not to say disciples of this sound are limited by its original parameters. Philadelphia's The Roots, for example, have embraced live musicianship as a way of extending the dynamic range in the live arena and as a nod to the original artists who were sampled by hip hop producers.

As well as performing under their own banner, The Roots have played a supporting role to numerous hip hop artists including Jay Z, Kanye West and Common. The band's drummer Amir 'Questlove' Thompson is the foremost drummer within the hip hop genre.

Chris 'Daddy' Dave is another excellent hip hop drummer. His ability to find a groove somewhere between straight quantization and heavy swing makes him an ideal player to learn from.

RECOMMENDED LISTENING

For classic East Coast drum programming listen to Nas' debut album *Illmatic* (1993). Also, the hip hop duos Pete Rock & CL Smooth's *The Main Ingredient* (1994) and Gang Starr's *Daily Operation* (1992) are strong examples from that period. Lastly, The Roots are best sampled via *How I Got Over* (2010).

The Nod

Neel Dhorajiwala

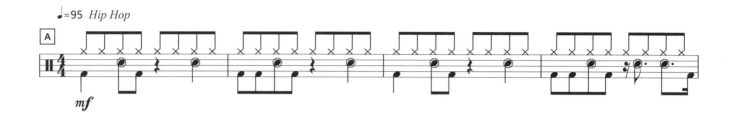

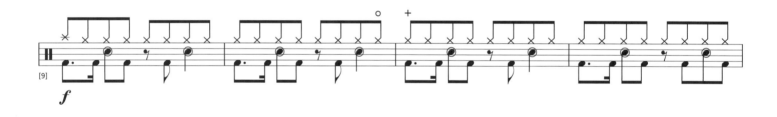

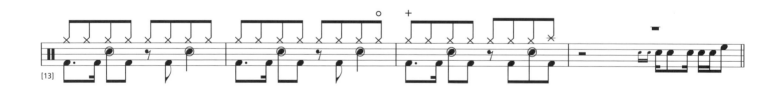

Drums Grade 4

18

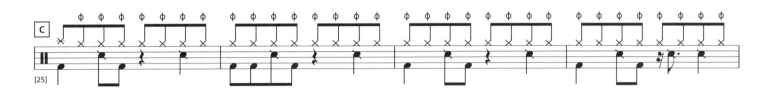

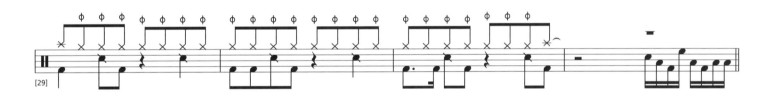

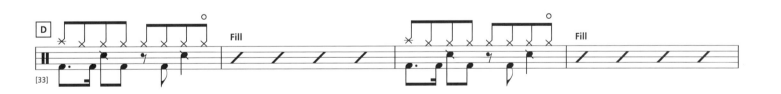

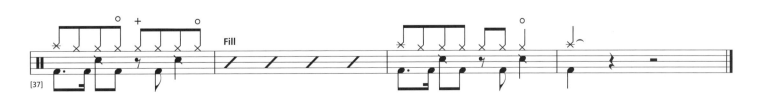

Drums Grade 4

Walkthrough

A Section (Bars 1–16)
This section features a hip hop beat with eighth-note hi-hats, cross stick backbeat and a varied bass drum pattern. The syncopated crash push in bar 15 and the fill in bar 16 prepare for the groove change in section B.

Bar 1 | *Cross stick*
The cross stick technique is common in hip hop but is used in many other styles too. To perform this technique, place the palm of your left hand on the snare drum head and strike the rim with your stick. Ensure that part of your palm remains in contact with the drum head because removing your hand before each stroke will affect the sound produced. Before attempting the full groove, practise this technique and find the area of the rim where the cross stick sounds most balanced and rounded. This area is known as the sweet spot. When playing a whole section using the cross stick, some drummers choose to use the 'butt' part of the drum stick because it produces a more defined sound.

Bar 4 | *Advanced co-ordination*
Co-ordinating the bottom part of the stave pattern with the hi-hats is one of the biggest challenges of this piece. Practise the cross stick/bass drum pattern without the hi-hat and ensure that all the rhythmic values are accurate. When adding the hi-hat pattern, pay attention to the pulse and work on achieving fluency within it.

Bar 16 | *Drag fill*
There are two beats of rest following the syncopated crash at the end of bar 15. The first snare stroke on beat three should be played with a drag, which means performing both grace notes before the main stroke. Use the natural bounce of the stick and a firm but not too tight grip in order to achieve accurate and fluent grace notes. The suggested sticking for this fill is shown in Fig. 1.

B Section (Bars 17–24)
Here the second main groove is introduced. This hip hop groove is based on 16th-note hi-hats using alternate sticking. From bar 18, you can develop the drum part stylistically. Make sure that you do so in keeping with the genre.

C Section (Bars 25–32)
The drum pattern intensifies in this section, with rim-shot snare and half open hi-hat.

Bar 25 | *Rim-shot*
The rim-shot technique is an integral part of drumming and is used in many styles. To produce a rim-shot you must strike the snare drum and surrounding rim at the same time. This will produce a louder and more pronounced sound.

The rim-shot should become a natural technique for you which can be performed on demand at any time. If you struggle to produce the rim-shot, try changing the height of your snare drum and the angle until you reach the position that suits you most (Fig. 2).

Bar 25 | *Half open hi-hat*
The vertical line through the open hi-hat mark indicates that the hi-hat should be only half open in this section. This can be done by tightening your hi-hat foot on the pedal. Ideally, the hi-hat cymbals will be consistently close to each other and produce a sizzling sound.

Bars 32 | *16th notes around the kit*
Two advanced approaches to fills are used here: dividing the strokes into uneven groups and using combinations of hands and feet. Practising this fill at a slower tempo will allow your body to learn and internalise the movement. The logical sticking pattern to use in this fill is L R F L R F R L (foot/bass drum marked as F). This combination of R L and L R lead follows the set-up of drums and allows you to develop further your control around the kit. Experiment with different stickings and move the fill around the kit in order to internalise the movement and rhythms.

D Section (Bars 33–40)
Now you have the opportunity to display your technical ability and understanding of the style. Listening to hip hop drummers such as The Roots' Ahmir 'Questlove' Thompson and Chris 'Daddy' Dave will give you ideas for improvised fills in this style.

Fig. 1: Drag fill

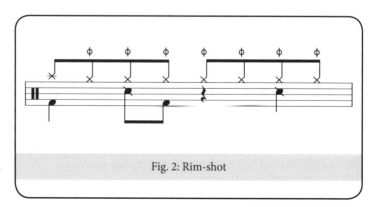

Fig. 2: Rim-shot

SONG TITLE: HAMMERBLOW

GENRE: METAL

TEMPO: 110 BPM

TECH FEATURES: 16TH-NOTE FILLS
& HI-HAT GROOVES
DYNAMICS
SYNCOPATION

COMPOSER: JASON BOWLD

PERSONNEL: JASON BOWLD (ALL PARTS)

OVERVIEW

'Hammerblow' is written in the nu metal style of bands such as Deftones, Korn and Limp Bizkit who emerged in the 1990s. It features 16th-note fills and hi-hat grooves, dynamics, syncopation and a military style crescendo among its techniques.

STYLE FOCUS

You need an awareness of syncopation or playing on the offbeat to play this style convincingly. It is essential to convey the funky nature of the grooves and fills that are evident in this area of metal. 'Hammerblow' features dynamics and builds that must be played with sensitivity and control in order to complement the backing. An ability to move around the kit seamlessly, making the transition from one section to another or from a groove to a fill, will help you to sound professional and demonstrate that you are thinking about the composition as a whole.

THE BIGGER PICTURE

Nu metal is a sub-genre of heavy metal that first came to prominence in the early 1990s and is a mixture of hip hop, punk, industrial, funk and electronica. The eclecticism of Faith No More, Jane's Addiction, Rage Against The Machine and others inspired the first wave of nu metal groups. However, Korn, Limp Bizkit and Deftones each achieved their sounds by adopting music technology in ways which their predecessors had not. The most obvious was the addition of a DJ to the standard rock group line-up: Limp Bizkit and Linkin Park's sounds both relied on turntables. The seven-string guitar was a relatively new addition to the guitarist's arsenal in the early 1990s and Korn, Limp Bizkit and Deftones all used its extra low string to add a bottom-end thump to their records. Samples, keyboards and the latest effects pedals were also used to make nu metal a truly new take on the genre.

RECOMMENDED LISTENING

Korn's self-titled debut (1994) was the starting shot for nu metal. The tracks 'Blind' and 'Ball Tongue' are a good introduction to the style. *Around The Fur* (1997) by Deftones features powerful drumming by Abe Cunningham, especially on 'Rickets' and 'Be Quiet And Drive'. For a funkier sound listen to John Otto's feel and groove on Limp Bizkit's *Significant Other* (1999). One of the lesser known drummers of this genre, Morgan Rose of Sevendust, shows off his tasteful style on *Home* (1999) and *Animosity* (2001).

Hammerblow

Jason Bowld

Walkthrough

A Section (Bars 1–8)
The A section's intro riff starts with stabs that lead into the main groove of this piece.

Bar 4 | *Stab fill*
After the initial unison snare and floor tom stabs, the fill here must be played with the correct 16th-note flow to make it sound convincing. (The suggested sticking pattern is shown in Fig. 1.)

Bars 5–8 | *Quarter-note crash groove*
There is a greater risk of timing errors here, especially with the syncopated bass drums because the crashes are played on quarter notes. Note their position on the 'a' of each beat.

B Section (Bars 9–20)
This verse section leads back to the A section. 16th-note hi-hats feature heavily here with solid backbeats.

Bars 9–15 | *16th-note hi-hat groove*
Your main focus on this groove should be to maintain its accented pulse throughout. Naturally, this is played on beats two and four but the hi-hats must also carry this on beats one and three. Be careful to not to let the bass drum pattern influence the hi-hat pattern.

Bar 16 | *16th-note fill*
In order to maintain flow when playing this type of fill follow this concept: every group of four 16th notes should be played as R L R L and if there is a rest on any of these notes, the remaining sticking pattern will be the same. In this fill there is a rest on the first 16th note of beat three. Start on the second 16th note with your left and alternate from there.

C Section (Bars 21–28)
This is the chorus which is made up of three grooves, each with a different feel.

Bars 21–22 | *Displaced snares*
This two bar groove features two main snare beats displaced from the usual two and four formula. They occur on the '&' of beat two and the 'e' of beat three and are then displaced forward in time by a 16th note in the subsequent bar.

Bars 23–26 | *Syncopated bass hits*
It can be quite difficult to place the syncopated bass hits in this groove because you must also play quarter notes on the hi-hat. Try counting the following rhythm to help with your timing: "1--a 2& 3e-a 4&" (Fig. 2).

Bars 27–28 | *Tom pattern*
Although it may look daunting, this pattern is quite simple

to play. Your left hand travels from snare to hi-tom while your right hand remains on the floor tom after the first crash. The bass drums break up the hand flow to give an almost linear feel.

Coda (Bars 29–34)
This is a reprise of the C section minus the tom pattern.

D Section (Bars 35–46)
The D section is the song's outro. It develops from a military style pattern on the snare into a loud stomping 4/4 groove.

Bars 35–42 | *Military crescendo*
The snare pattern shown in bars 35 and 36 can be used as a template to develop throughout this section. The crescendo must build steadily and the pattern can be embellished with doubles and presses on the snare to enhance the military feel. As long as the main accents on beat one and the '&' of two are followed, you will have a lot of scope to be creative in this section. The flam on beat four of bar 42 is crucial to highlight the pause in the music.

Bars 43–45 | *Playing loud*
This is the loudest point of the song and should be played as such. However, playing loud is often misinterpreted as playing faster and in these instances the click becomes your best friend, especially when only quarter notes are being played in the groove.

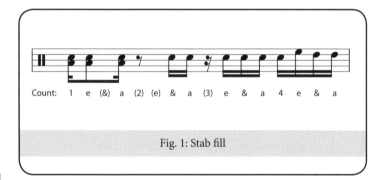

Fig. 1: Stab fill

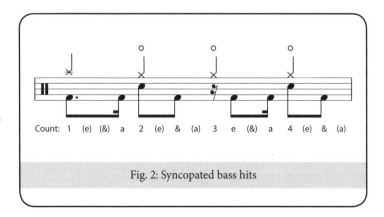

Fig. 2: Syncopated bass hits

SONG TITLE: JAHMAKE SKA

GENRE: SKA

TEMPO: 118 BPM

TECH FEATURES: OFFBEAT HI-HAT PATTERN
SYNCOPATION
CROSS-STICK ON THE SNARE

COMPOSER: KITA STEUER

PERSONNEL: STUART RYAN (GTR)
HENRY THOMAS (BASS)
NOAM LEDERMAN (DRUMS)
ROSS STANLEY (KEYS)
FERGUS GERRAND (PERC)
FULL FAT HORNS (BRASS)

OVERVIEW

'Jahmake Ska' is a track in the style of original Jamaican ska artists such as Desmond Dekker and Prince Buster and later ska groups like The Specials. It features an offbeat hi-hat pattern, syncopation and cross stick on the snare among its techniques.

STYLE FOCUS

The distinctive feel of ska is instantly recognisable for its hi-hat patterns that play on the offbeat rather than *on* the beat, as is usually the case in rock 'n' roll and R&B. In traditional ska, the drummers often play with a cross stick on the snare instead of a conventional stroke and many ska drummers have a timbale in their kit for accents. The style requires a high level of syncopation to balance the beats on the bass and snare with the hi-hat patterns.

THE BIGGER PICTURE

Ska emerged in Jamaica in the early 1960s, inspired by R&B and rock 'n' roll but with a unique feel based on the rhythms of African nyabinghi drumming. Kingston musician Prince Buster (considered one of the most important figures in ska and rocksteady)

and his contemporaries ruled the Jamaican dancehalls and inspired the popular 2 Tone movement in Britain during the 1970s when bands like Madness, The Specials, Bad Manners and The Selecter took ska into the charts. The third wave of ska bands added punk to the sound, led by Operation Ivy, The Mighty Mighty Bosstones and The Toasters.

A later movement during the 1990s, which began in Southern California, had its moment in the spotlight with the success of No Doubt and Sublime. Since its birth in Jamaica in the 1960s, Jamaican ska has become a global phenomenon with Witchery Skank and Tokyo Ska Paradise Orchestra performing ska in Japan, and Los Fabulosos Cadillacs in Argentina.

RECOMMENDED LISTENING

The Jamaican ska scene was dominated by singles. A compilation album like *Trojan Presents Ska* (2011) will offer you a sample of all the major artists of the era. Of the 2 Tone bands, Bad Manners' single 'Walking In The Sunshine' and The Specials' self-titled debut album (1979) are highlights. Operation Ivy's *Energy* (1989) remains a fan favourite even though the band split up before its release. For an in-depth look at ska, rocksteady and reggae drumming watch Gil Sharone's excellent DVD *Wicked Beats* (2010).

Jahmake Ska

Kita Steuer

Walkthrough

A Section (Bars 1–16)
This section features the first ska groove of the piece, which consists of offbeat hi-hats and a bass drum/cross stick pattern typical of the genre. There is a pick-up fill before the groove starts in bar 1.

Pick-up bar | *Counting the pick-up*
In this piece there is a two beat pick-up fill before the groove starts in bar 1. The first bass drum stroke is placed on the third beat in the second bar of the spoken count-in. There are no other instruments that play this pattern. Therefore, use the backing track and your inner pulse.

Bar 1 | *Cross stick*
The cross stick technique is common in ska but it is used in many other styles of drumming too. In order to perform this technique, place the palm of your left hand on the snare drum head and strike the rim with your stick. Ensure that part of your palm always remains in contact with the drum head, because removing your hand before each stroke will affect the sound produced. Before attempting the full groove, practise this technique and find the area of the rim where the cross stick sounds most balanced and rounded. This area is known as the sweet spot.

Bar 2 | *Advanced co-ordination*
Co-ordinating the bottom part of the stave pattern with the offbeat hi-hats is one of the biggest challenges of this piece. Practise the cross stick/bass drum pattern without the hi-hat and ensure that all the rhythmic values are accurate. This syncopated pattern and the lack of parts to play on beat four makes this a difficult passage to play. When adding the hi-hat, pay attention to the pulse and work on achieving a fluent groove. The drum voices must be balanced and the cross stick needs to sound convincing (Fig. 1).

B Section (Bars 17–24)
The second main groove is introduced here. This is a ska meets reggae type beat with bass drum/cross stick on beats two and four. The hi-hat remains on the offbeats with occasional open hi-hats and 16th-note phrases.

Bar 17 | *Closing the hi-hat*
The '+' above the eighth-note rests indicates that you should close the hi-hat by tightening your foot on the hi-hat pedal. This must be well synchronised with the backing track or else the flow of the groove will be affected.

C Section (Bars 25–36)
The first four bars of this section are a build-up for the trombone solo that starts in bar 29. The groove consists of syncopated bass drums and displaced snares.

Bar 25 | *Syncopated rhythms*
The phrase presented in this bar can be counted as "1 – – a – – – & 2 – – a – – – &". It might be helpful to listen to the full version of this piece to understand the syncopation before playing it. Remember that your three limbs must be played in perfect unison without any unnecessary flams (Fig. 2).

Bars 25–28 | *Long crescendo*
In these bars you need to apply a gradual dynamic change from moderately soft ***mp*** to loud ***f***.

Bars 29–36 | *Trombone solo*
In this section you will need to develop the groove according to the style, personal interpretation and instruments used on the backing track. The drums' development should support the soloist and provide an inspiring base for improvisation.

D Section (Bars 37–49)
This is a reprise of the A section with a few added fills and cross stick that develops to snare. Keep the hi-hat light. All rhythmic variations and tom fills must sound convincing.

Bars 48–49 | *Sticking*
For maximum projection, play the last four eighth notes of these bars with alternate sticking, starting with your right hand. This will lead to hitting the open hi-hat (bar 48) and crash (bar 49) with your left hand. If you prefer to use different sticking, feel free to do so but ensure that the fill is fluent and synchronised well with the track.

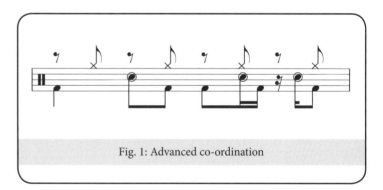

Fig. 1: Advanced co-ordination

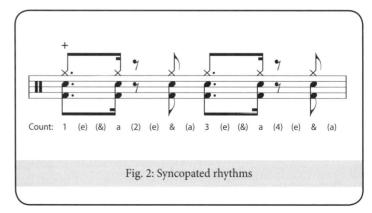

Fig. 2: Syncopated rhythms

Technical Exercises

In this section the examiner will ask you to play a selection of exercises drawn from each of the four groups shown below. In addition there is a Fill exercise which you will play using the designated backing track on the CD. You do not need to memorise the exercises (and can use the book in the exam) but the examiner will be looking for the speed of your response.

The stickings shown (L & R) are there as a guide for right handed drummers. Left handed drummers should reverse the sticking patterns. **All exercises must be played to a metronome click.** Groups A–D should be played at $\quarternote = 75$.

Group A: Single and Double Strokes
Single and double strokes in eighth notes, eighth-note triplets and 16th notes. To be played first time with singles and second with doubles

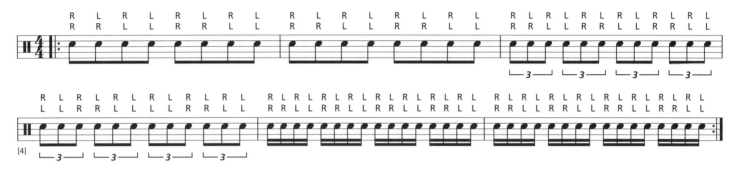

Group B: Paradiddles
Single paradiddle in 16th notes using the whole kit

Triple paradiddle in 16th notes using the whole kit

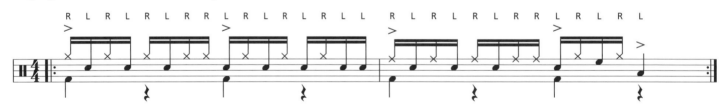

Group C: Flams and Ruffs
Flam tap and ruffs in quarter notes

Group D: Hands and Feet Patterns (sticking shown is optional)

A. Pattern 1

B. Pattern 2

C. Pattern 3

D. Pattern 4

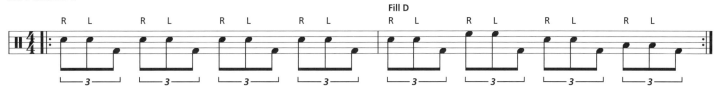

Group E: Fill

In the exam you will be asked to play the three bar groove shown followed by the second bar of one of the hands and feet patterns (Fills A–D) shown in Group D above chosen by the examiner. The snare is to be played with rim-shots and ghost notes. You will perform this exercise to the backing track on the CD with a repeat. The tempo is ♩= 80.

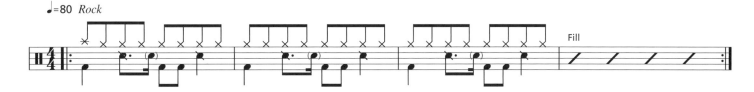

Sight Reading

In this section you have a choice between either a sight reading test or an improvisation & interpretation test (see facing page). You will be asked to prepare a sight reading test which will be given to you by the examiner. The test is an eight bar groove using the whole kit. At this level there is an element of improvisation. This is in the form of a two bar development. The examiner will allow you 90 seconds to prepare it and will set the tempo for you. The tempo is ♩= 80–120.

Improvisation & Interpretation

You will be asked to play a written two bar groove, vary it in the following four bars and then improvise a two bar solo. The test will be played to a backing track using the bass drum, hi-hat (closed and open), snare drum, ride cymbal and crash cymbal. You have 30 seconds to prepare then you will be allowed to practise during the first playing of the backing track, before playing it to the examiner on the second playing of the backing track. This test is continuous with a one bar count-in at the beginning and after the practice session. The tempo is ♩=80–120.

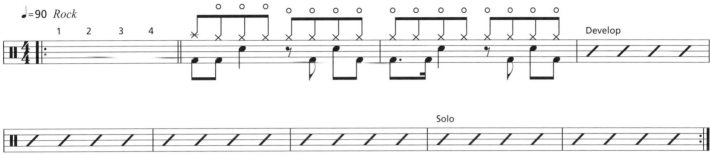

[5]

Ear Tests

There are two ear tests in this grade. The examiner will play each test to you twice. You will find one example of each type of test printed below.

Test 1: Fill Playback and Recognition

The examiner will play you a one bar fill in common time played on the snare drum. You will play back the fill on the snare drum. You will then identify the fill from three printed examples shown to you by the examiner. You will hear the test twice.

Each time the test is played it is preceded by a one bar count in. There will be a short gap for you to practise. Next you will hear the vocal count in and you will then play the fill to the click. The tempo is ♩ = 70.

Test 2: Groove Recall

The examiner will play you a two-bar groove played on the bass drum, hi-hat (open and closed), crash cymbal, ride cymbal, bell of ride, cross stick and snare. This is a two bar groove repeated. You will hear the test twice. You will be asked to play the groove back on the drum voices indicated for four bars then identify the style from three choices given by the examiner.

Each time the test is played it is preceded by a one bar vocal count-in. The tempo is ♩ = 80–120.

A: Rock
B: Jazz
C: Latin

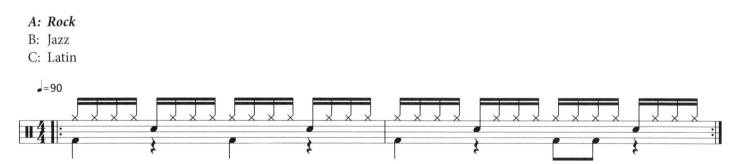

General Musicianship Questions

In this part of the exam you will be asked five questions. Four of these questions will be about general music knowledge and the fifth question will be asked about your instrument.

Music Knowledge

The examiner will ask you four music knowledge questions based on a piece of music that you have played in the exam. You will nominate the piece of music about which the questions will be asked.

In Grade 4 you will be asked:

- Drum voices on the stave

- The meaning of the time signature marking

- The meaning of bpm markings

- Repeat marks, first and second time bars, D.C., D.S., al Coda and al fine markings

- All note values used in the chosen piece

- Equivalent rests

- One type of rudiment that can be used stylistically in the solo or development section of the piece

- Use of drum voices, rhythms and techniques in drum solo sections

Instrument Knowledge

The examiner will also ask you one question regarding your instrument.

In Grade 4 you will be asked to identify/explain:

- Any part of the drum kit and drumstick

- How to tune the drum kit

- Cross stick, choke cymbal, bell of ride and accent

Further Information

Tips on how to approach this part of this exam can be found in the *Syllabus Guide* for Drums, the Rockschool *Drums Companion Guide* and on the Rockschool website: *www.rockschool.co.uk*.

Entering Rockschool Exams

Entering a Rockschool exam is easy. You may enter either online at *www.rockschool.co.uk* or by downloading and filling in an exam entry form. Information on current exam fees can be obtained from Rockschool online or by calling +44 (0)845 460 4747.

- You should enter for your exam when you feel ready.

- You may enter for any one of the three examination periods shown below with their closing dates:

EXAMINATION PERIODS

PERIOD	DURATION	CLOSING DATE
Period A	1st February to 31st March	1st December
Period B	1st May to 31st July	1st April
Period C	23rd October to 15th December	1st October

These dates apply from 1st September 2012 until further notice

- The full Rockschool examination terms and conditions can be downloaded from our website. The information shown below is a summary.

- Please complete your entry with the information required. Fill in the type and level of exam and instrument, along with the examination period and year. Paper entry forms should be sent with a cheque or postal order (payable to Rockschool Ltd) to the address shown on the entry form. Entry forms sent by post will be acknowledged either by letter or email, while all entries made online will automatically be acknowledged by email.

- Applications received after the expiry of the closing date, whether made by post or online, may be accepted subject to the payment of a late fee.

- Rockschool will allocate your exam to a specific centre and you will receive notification of the exam showing a date, location and time, as well as advice on what to bring to the centre. We endeavour to give you four weeks notice ahead of your exam date.

- You should inform Rockschool of any cancellations or alterations to the schedule as soon as you can because it may not be possible to transfer entries from one centre, or one period, to another without the payment of an additional fee.

- Please bring your music book and CD to the exam. You may use photocopied music if this helps you avoid awkward page turns. The examiner will sign each book during each examination. Please note, you may be barred from taking an exam if you use someone else's music.

- You should aim to arrive for your exam 15 minutes before the time stated on the schedule. Guitarists and bass players should get ready to enter the exam room by taking their instrument from its case and tuning up. This will help with the smooth running of each exam day.

- Each Grade 4 exam is scheduled to last 25 minutes. You can use a small proportion of this time to set up and check the sound levels.

- You will receive a copy of the examiner's marksheet two to three weeks after the exam. If you have passed you will also receive a Rockschool certificate of achievement.

Drums Grade 4 Marking Schemes

ELEMENT	PASS	MERIT	DISTINCTION
Performance Piece 1	12–14 out of 20	15–17 out of 20	18+ out of 20
Performance Piece 2	12–14 out of 20	15–17 out of 20	18+ out of 20
Performance Piece 3	12–14 out of 20	15–17 out of 20	18+ out of 20
Technical Exercises	9–10 out of 15	11–12 out of 15	13+ out of 15
Either **Sight Reading** *or* **Improvisation & Interpretation**	6 out of 10	7–8 out of 10	9+ out of 10
Ear Tests	6 out of 10	7–8 out of 10	9+ out of 10
General Musicianship Questions	3 out of 5	4 out of 5	5 out of 5
TOTAL MARKS	60%+	74%+	90%+

PERFORMANCE CERTIFICATES | GRADES 1–8

ELEMENT	PASS	MERIT	DISTINCTION
Performance Piece 1	12–14 out of 20	15–17 out of 20	18+ out of 20
Performance Piece 2	12–14 out of 20	15–17 out of 20	18+ out of 20
Performance Piece 3	12–14 out of 20	15–17 out of 20	18+ out of 20
Performance Piece 4	12–14 out of 20	15–17 out of 20	18+ out of 20
Performance Piece 5	12–14 out of 20	15–17 out of 20	18+ out of 20
TOTAL MARKS	60%+	75%+	90%+

Drums Notation Explained

BASS DRUM & TOMS

| Bass drum | Floor tom | Medium tom | High tom |

SNARE

| Snare | Ghost snare | Rim-shot | Cross stick | Buzz snare |

Strike snare drum and surrounding rim at same time *Place palm on snare drum head and strike rim with stick*

HI-HAT

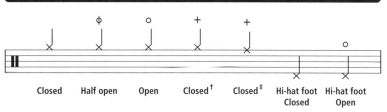

| Closed | Half open | Open | Closed † | Closed ‡ | Hi-hat foot Closed | Hi-hat foot Open |

† *Used on the first closed hi-hat that follows an open hi-hat*

‡ *The hi-hat is closed without being struck. Note that the hi-hat closed (cross) symbol may appear above drum voices other than the hi-hat (as shown above). This simply means another drum voice is being played at the same moment that the hi-hat is being closed.*

OTHER CYMBALS

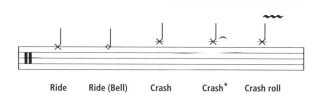

| Ride | Ride (Bell) | Crash | Crash* | Crash roll |

***Allow all cymbals to ring on** unless explicitly stopped, as indicated by the keyword **'Choke'**. Occasionally ties may be used (*) to emphasise that cymbals should be allowed to ring on. This can avoid confusion during syncopations and pushes.*

GENERAL MUSIC NOTATION

Accentuate note (play it louder).

Slashes are used to demarcate bars during solos, fills, developments and other ad lib. sections.

D.%. al Coda

Go back to the sign (%), then play until the bar marked **To Coda** ⊕ then skip to the section marked ⊕ **Coda**.

Repeat the bars between the repeat signs.

D.C. al Fine

Go back to the beginning of the song and play until the bar marked **Fine** (end).

When a repeated section has different endings, play the first ending only the first time and the second ending only the second time.

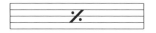

Repeat the previous bar. In higher grades these may also be marked *sim.* or *cont. sim.*

Repeat the previous two bars. In higher grades these may also be marked *sim.* or *cont. sim.*

In rudiments, each stem slash subdivides the note value by half.

MUSICAL TERMS WITH SPECIFIC EXAMINATION DEFINITIONS

Fill Play an individual, stylistic fill.

Cont. sim. Continue in a similar way but vary the pattern slightly.

Develop Extend the musical part in a stylistically appropriate manner.

Rit. (ritardando) Gradually slow the tempo.

SONG TITLE: GEEK
GENRE: POP PUNK
TEMPO: 137 BPM

TECH FEATURES: SWUNG EIGHTH NOTES
CRESCENDO
TRIPLETS

COMPOSER: JAMES UINGS

PERSONNEL: STUART RYAN (GTR)
DAVE MARKS (BASS)
NOAM LEDERMAN (DRUMS)

OVERVIEW

'Geek' is a pop punk piece created in the style of Green Day, The Offspring and Billy Talent. It features a crescendo, ghosting, and triplet and swung eighth notes among its techniques.

STYLE FOCUS

Punk requires an awareness of musicality and versatility. Occasionally, as with 'Geek', a shuffle feel is required to buoy the groove with extra bounce. Many drummers underestimate how tricky a shuffle is to pull off. In fact, some say you can judge a drummer's skill by how accurately he is able to play one. With three eighth-note triplets played per beat instead of two (as in a straight groove), you need to watch out for any timing errors.

THE BIGGER PICTURE

A shuffle feel may seem out of place in a punk song but as far back as the 1970s groups like The Clash were absorbing influences from other genres.

Green Day, in much the same way as The Clash, began in a narrow punk field then signed to a major record label and assimilated techniques and songwriting tricks that were alien to their genre. The group's frontman and guitarist, Billie Joe Armstrong, professed a love of the rock bands The Who and Cheap Trick who obviously influenced his approach to songwriting. He also grew up in a musical household with a father who played jazz drums and recalls singing jazz standards as a child.

Green Day's contemporaries The Offspring had a metal edge to their sound and became more open to outside influences as their career progressed. *Americana*, their fifth album released in 1998, bore the mark of various musical styles from new wave to hip hop, rocksteady to mariachi.

In the 2000s, Canadian four piece Billy Talent demonstrated that punk could be shaped by influences as unlikely as Van Halen and The Police.

RECOMMENDED LISTENING

To gain an understanding of punk style drumming, listen to the album *Setting Sons* (1979) by The Jam where Rick Buckler's playing is a foretaste of Tre Cool's from Green Day. For a shuffle similar to that of 'Geek', listen to 'Basket Case' and 'Longview' from Green Day's *Dookie* (1994).

Geek (Grade 5 Preview)

James Uings

♩=137 *Pop Punk*

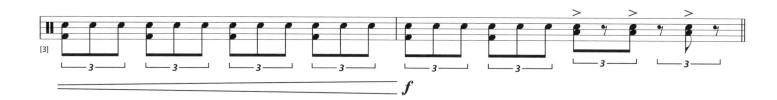

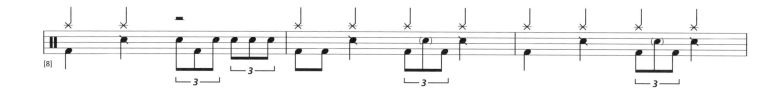

[36]

F **Drum Solo** (8 bars)

[39]

[43]

G **Guitar Solo** (12 bars)

[47]

Develop

[50]

[53]

[56]

Bass Solo (8 bars)

Walkthrough (Grade 5 Preview)

A Section (Bars 1–4)

This introduction includes a long crescendo build-up on the snare, floor tom and bass drum. Remember that the rhythmic guidance above bar 1 indicates that all eighth notes should be swung.

Bars 1–3 | *Dynamic control*

Start playing soft strokes on the snare and floor tom. Keep the drumsticks close to the drum head and perform these as a tap. Gradually lift your arms and allow the strokes to increase naturally in dynamic level until you build up to *f*.

Bar 4 | *Accents*

Lift your arms higher in order to achieve the accents and aim to hit the middle of the drum for maximum projection.

B Section (Bars 5–13)

The first main groove is introduced here, in the B section. This groove is led by the crash and includes rim-shots and ghost notes on the snare.

Bar 5 | *Rim-shot*

When performing a rim-shot you must strike the snare drum and surrounding rim at the same time in order to achieve a louder and more prominent sound. If you are struggling to produce the rim-shot, try changing the height and angle of your snare drum until you reach the position that suits you best (Fig. 1).

Bar 5 | *Ghost notes*

Ghost notes are marked with brackets and played most commonly on the snare drum. The dynamic level of the ghost notes should be much lower than the non-ghosted snare strokes.

Bar 8 | *Triplet fill with hand/foot combination*

There are six triplet notes to play in this fill. With the exception of the second, these should all be played on the snare. Experiment and choose the sticking option that suits your technique best. You can achieve fluency by practising similar hand/foot combinations at various speeds (Fig. 2).

C Section (Bars 14–21)

In this section a similar snare and bass drum pattern is played with quarter-note hi-hats.

Bar 14 | *Rim to ghost*

This is an important technique in drumming, where a ghost note is played after a rim-shot backbeat. After performing the rim-shot, allow your stick to bounce once but keep your hand close to the drum head. This will naturally create the ghost snare and allow you to focus on your timing.

D Section (Bars 22–29)

In this section the hi-hat pattern should be played as swung eighth notes. From bar 26 the closed hi-hat sound should be changed to half open in preparation for the next section.

Bar 23 | *Wrist movement*

Try playing the fast swung eighth notes and allow your wrist to move up and down. Coordinate your arm movement with your wrist and aim to produce the strokes without expending too much energy. Solid and reliable stick grip is essential here.

E Section (Bars 30–38)

This is similar to the B section but the groove is played on open hi-hat instead of the crash cymbal.

F, G & H sections (Bars 39–66)

These sections are the drums, guitar and bass solos. The eight bar drum solo is your opportunity to demonstrate your technical ability and musicality. Listening to the drummer Tre Cool (Green Day) will give you ideas for improvisation and development in this style.

I Section (Bars 67–78)

This groove is similar to the B section but with minor variations. The improvised fill in bar 77 leads to the final unison phrase in bar 78.

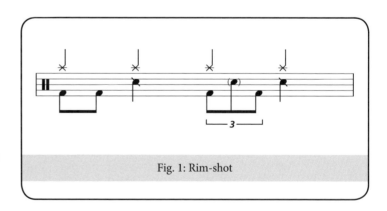

Fig. 1: Rim-shot

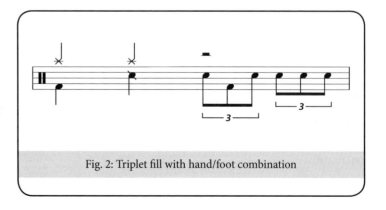

Fig. 2: Triplet fill with hand/foot combination